W9-BXW-750

SPIDER-MAN
SECRET WARS

SPIDER-MAN
SECRET WARS

Writer: **Paul Tobin**

Pencilers: **Patrick Scherberger**
with **Clayton Henry** (Issue #4)

Inkers: **Terry Pallot**
with **Clayton Henry**
and **Patrick Scherberger** (Issue #4)

Colorist: **Brad Anderson**

Letterer: **Dave Sharpe**

Cover Artists: **Patrick Scherberger**
with **Christina Strain,**
Chris Sotomayor,
Veronica Gandini
& **Jean-Francois Beaulieu**

Assistant Editor: **Michael Horwitz**

Editor: **Nathan Cosby**

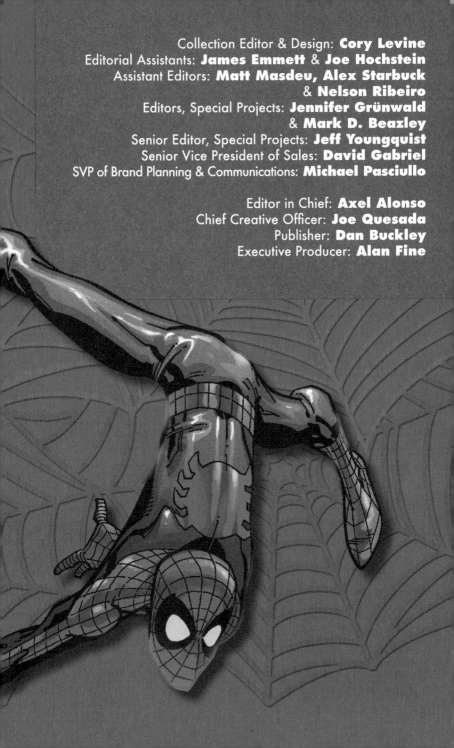

Collection Editor & Design: **Cory Levine**
Editorial Assistants: **James Emmett** & **Joe Hochstein**
Assistant Editors: **Matt Masdeu, Alex Starbuck**
& **Nelson Ribeiro**
Editors, Special Projects: **Jennifer Grünwald**
& **Mark D. Beazley**
Senior Editor, Special Projects: **Jeff Youngquist**
Senior Vice President of Sales: **David Gabriel**
SVP of Brand Planning & Communications: **Michael Pasciullo**

Editor in Chief: **Axel Alonso**
Chief Creative Officer: **Joe Quesada**
Publisher: **Dan Buckley**
Executive Producer: **Alan Fine**

QUICK ANSWER: THE *MOLECULE MAN* DROPS A *MOUNTAIN* ON THEM.

LONGER ANSWER, WE WERE *KIDNAPPED* FROM EARTH BY A SEEMINGLY *OMNIPOTENT* ENTITY KNOWN AS THE *BEYONDER.*

AND IT WASN'T ONLY *HEROES.* THE BEYONDER BROUGHT ON THE *BAD GUYS.* WE HEROES ARE SUPPOSED TO *FIGHT* THEM, WHICH WOULD BE EASIER IF THEY WOULD LAY OFF WITH THE *MOUNTAIN-DROPPING.*

THE BEYONDER DESTROYED AN *ENTIRE GALAXY,* USING ITS REMAINS TO CREATE A BATTLE-WORLD. HE PUMPED US ALL HERE AND RANG THE *STARTING BELL.* THERE'S A FABULOUS PRIZE FOR THE WINNERS.

AND RIGHT NOW, IT'S LOOKING LIKE THE *LOSERS* GET A MOUNTAIN.

THREE HOURS AGO, THIS WHOLE NIGHTMARE *REALLY* STARTED ROLLING.

CAPTAIN MARVEL, YOU MOVE AT THE SPEED OF LIGHT, SO YOU'LL SCOUT AHEAD.

CAN DO.

THIS COULD GET *DANGEROUS.* WE *SURE* IT'S THE RIGHT THING?

YOU CAN STAY BACK AT THE *BASE* IF YOU WANT.

DIDN'T SAY THAT. WE *DO* NEED TO KNOW WHAT THE BAD GUYS ARE UP TO. BUT THE BEYONDER GAVE US *MACHINES* THAT CAN *MONITOR* THE *WHOLE* WORLD.

WOULDN'T IT BE *SMARTER* TO STAY AT BASE? *USE* THEM?

A COMMANDER SHOULD NEVER ENTIRELY RELY ON TECHNOLOGY. FIRSTHAND INTELLIGENCE IS THE ONLY REAL INTELLIGENCE.

YEAH. *SECONDHAND* INTELLIGENCE IS *DUMB.*

KEEP QUIET. THERE'S THE ENCHANTRESS.

GREAT. A *DIVINE SORCERESS.*

YOU KNOW, THE CARDS SEEM STACKED *AGAINST* US.

HOW SO?

WHAT'S SHE DOING ANYWAY?

WHO KNOWS? STARING AT FISH. COMPOSING POETRY. CRAFTING A SPELL THAT WILL SPREAD OUR ATOMS OVER THE UNIVERSE.

THIS COULD BE BAD.

I DON'T LIKE POETRY.

WHAT ARE ALL THOSE TENDRIL THINGS?

NOT SURE. DIFFICULT TO TELL WHAT A SORCERESS IS--

LOOK OUT!

UNHHH!

BIG DEAL! I AM A POWER GREATER THAN I CAN COMPREHEND!

WHAT? HOW CAN YOU STILL BE ALIVE?!

THESE BOLTS ARE POWERFUL ENOUGH TO KILL A HORSE!

A HORSE? YOU SEE A SADDLE ON ME?

THWAKKT

THEY'RE DISSOLVING.

YAY! GOODBYE AND GOOD RIDDANCE TO THE MAGIC GARDEN HOSES!

NICE WORK, HULK.

THANKS.

YEAH, AND WHAT A GREAT LINE! YOU SEE A SADDLE ON ME? SOUNDS TOUGH! I'M GOING TO START USING IT IN EVERY-DAY LIFE.

IF THE SCHOOL BULLY PUSHES ME DOWN AT RECESS, I'LL LOOK HIM IN THE EYE AND--

SHUT UP! SHUT... UP!

WHY DO YOU ALWAYS HAVE TO BE JOKING?! CAN'T YOU JUST SHUT UP?!

UH, I JOKE BECAUSE I GET *NERVOUS*. LIKE *NOW*.

SO...WANNA HEAR A *COMICAL ANECDOTE*?

LET'S CALM *DOWN* HERE. WE'RE ALL ON THE *SAME* TEAM.

GUYS...THE *WRECKING CREW* ARE COMING UP *FAST!*

THE *ENCHANTRESS* MUST HAVE GOTTEN OFF A *DISTRESS CALL.*

DOUBT IT. *SHE* COULD HAVE JUST *TELEPORTED* THEM HERE.

DOESN'T *MATTER*. WE CAN'T *FIGHT* THEM. THEY'RE TOO POWERFUL.

NOBODY IS TOO *POWERFUL* FOR *ME!* I'LL *SMASH* THEM ALL!

IT'S NOT ALL ABOUT *YOU!* THE WRECKING CREW ARE TOO POWERFUL FOR *ME!*

SO *RUN AWAY!* WHO'S ASKING YOU TO *STAY?*

NOT AGAIN. I *MEAN* IT. WE'RE ALL IN THIS *TOGETHER*.

UNTIL WE FIND A WAY *OFF* THIS *BATTLE-WORLD*, WE'RE ALL WE *HAVE*, AND WE *MUST* BELIEVE IN EACH OTHER.

BRUCE...I CAN'T POSSIBLY IMAGINE THE *TORTURE* YOU'RE ENDURING, *TRAPPED* IN THAT BODY, WITH WHAT IT DOES TO YOUR *MIND*. BUT WE *NEED* YOU.

WE NEED YOU TO DO WHAT'S *SMART*.

I COULD *SMASH* THEM, CAP. I *COULD*.

YOU *CAN'T* CONCEIVE OF THE *POWER* THAT'S--

NO. YOU'RE RIGHT. I'M GETTING *SWEPT UP* IN THE *EMOTIONS*.

WE SHOULD *GO*.

AND *FAST*. THE WRECKING CREW ARE--

WAIT! WHERE'S THE *ENCHANTRESS*?

SHE'S *GONE!* SHE MUST HAVE TELEPORTED AWAY WHILE I WAS... BEING MAD.

I'M SORRY. THIS IS MY FAULT.

NAWW. WITHOUT *YOU*, WE'D HAVE LOST A FIGHT TO A *GARDEN HOSE*.

I DOUBT THAT. CAPTAIN AMERICA ALWAYS FINDS A WAY.

REGARDLESS, LET'S GET AWAY FROM HERE. WE NEED TO FIND SOMEPLACE SAFE.

NOT TOO LONG BEFORE THE ATTACK, I WAS ARGUING WITH CAPTAIN AMERICA ABOUT THE HULK.

WHY IS HE SO *ANGRY* ALL THE TIME?

HE'S *NOT* ANGRY ALL THE TIME.

OKAY, *FINE*, SO HE'S *NOT* ANGRY ALL THE TIME. IT'S JUST THAT I TEND TO NOTICE WHEN HE *IS* ANGRY, BECAUSE HE COULD *PICK ME UP AND THROW ME INTO SPACE.*

BUT HE *WOULDN'T.*

BUT HE *COULD.*

THAT'S A *BAD* GAME TO PLAY.

IF YOU START THINKING LIKE THAT, YOU END UP THINKING I MIGHT ATTACK YOU.

BUT YOU *WOULDN'T.*

EXACTLY MY POINT.

YOU'RE *CHANGING* THE *SUBJECT.* WE'RE TALKING ABOUT THE *HULK.* HE'S LOSING HIS GRIP ON THE *BRUCE BANNER* PERSONA. LETTING THE *ANGER* CONTROL HIM.

WRONG.

BUT *DOCTOR DOOM* AND HIS *UN-MERRY MEN* DECIDED TO CRASH OUR PARTY, AND CUT INTO MY *SULKING* TIME.

TITANIA TOOK *REED* AND *BEN* OUT OF ACTION. *JOHNNY* WAS STILL FIGHTING, BUT HE WAS BUSTED UP.

SHE-HULK WAS AMBUSHED BY *VOLCANA.*

DOCTOR OCTOPUS CLIPPED *CAPTAIN MARVEL,* KNOCKING HER UNCONSCIOUS. WE COULD HAVE USED HER *SPEED.*

IRON MAN AND I HAD THE MISFORTUNE OF BEING VISITED BY *ULTRON.*

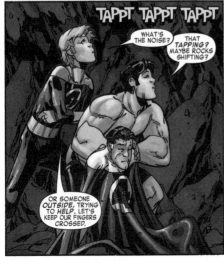

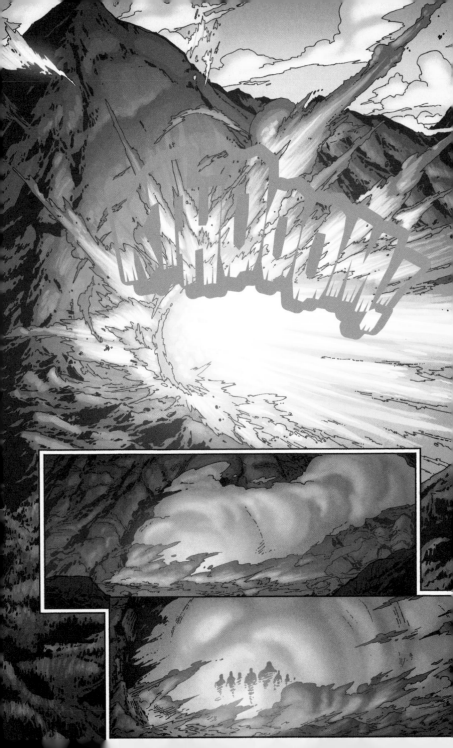

...END

#2

STAY BEHIND THE BARRICADES!

LET THEM COME TO YOU!

PROTECT EACH OTHER'S BACKS!

IF WE'RE STRONG, WE'LL MAKE IT THROUGH THIS!

KEEP SWINGING! FIGHT HARD!

THESE ALIENS ARE COWARDS!

KNOCK ENOUGH OF THEM DOWN, AND THEY'LL ALL GIVE UP!

SO KEEP KNOCKING THEM DOWN!

AND DO WHAT YOU--

THERE IS LITTLE NEED TO TELL ONE SUCH AS I HOW TO DO BATTLE.

EARTH'S GREATEST HEROES

WORLD'S VILEST VILLAINS

FORCED TO WAGE WAR

FOR THE ULTIMATE PRIZE

LOCKHEED IS COMING BACK!

THEY'RE ALMOST HERE! GET READY!

WELCOME TO DENVER'S DIAMOND ELECTRONICS... WHERE YOU'RE THE STAR!

FOR DENVER!

SO, THIS IS *DENVER,* HUH?

YEP. WHEN THE *BEYONDER* CREATED THIS *BATTLEWORLD,* HE APPARENTLY NABBED *DENVER, COLORADO.*

ANY IDEA *WHY?*

MAYBE HE JUST THOUGHT IT WAS A PRETTY CITY.

IT *IS* NICE. AND EVERYONE SEEMS TO BE FAIRLY CALM, AT LEAST FOR A GROUP OF PEOPLE SUDDENLY FINDING THEMSELVES *AND THEIR* CITY ON AN ALIEN PLANET.

PART OF THAT'S BECAUSE OF *REED'S* PLAN. HE BELIEVES PEOPLE DEAL WITH TROUBLE BETTER WHEN THEY KNOW THE *FACTS.*

THAT'S WHY HE ASKED US TO COME HERE?

RIGHT. AND WHY HE CREATED THESE *HOLO-PROJECTORS.*

PEOPLE OF *DENVER.* YOUR CITY IS NOW ON A PLANET CALLED *BATTLEWORLD,* TRANSPORTED BY A POWERFUL BEING KNOWN AS THE *BEYONDER.*

THE *BEYONDER* HAS BROUGHT TEAMS OF BOTH VILLAINS AND HEROES TO THIS PLANET, SETTING US IN BATTLE AGAINST EACH OTHER.

AS SOON AS WE HEROES WIN, DENVER WILL BE RESTORED TO EARTH.

AND WE WILL WIN. WE ARE *WINNING.*

KEEP CALM. KEEP *FAITH.* WE ARE FIGHTING FOR YOU.

SPIDER-MAN?

HUH?

IS THAT *REALLY* YOU?

UHHM, *YEAH*. REALLY ME. EVERY TIME.

YOU'D BE *SURPRISED*. HALF THE NEIGHBORHOOD KIDS *LOVE* DRESSING UP LIKE YOU.

HELLO. I'M *JANET*. AND *YOU* ARE...?

BEN GRIMM.

BEN GRIMM? THE *THING*?

THE *ONE AND ONLY*, BUT NOT VERY *ROCKY* RIGHT NOW. SOMETHIN' ABOUT THIS *WORLD*, IT *CHANGES* ME.

IT'S CHANGING *ALL* OF US. GIVES ME THE *SHIVERS*.

LISTEN, I JUST STEPPED OUTSIDE TO ROUND UP MY SON HUBERT FOR *DINNER*. YOU TWO EATEN YET?

WE'RE JUST HERE TO MAKE SURE MR. FANTASTIC'S HOLO-PROJECTIONS ARE WORKING.

AND THEY *ARE*. YOUR JOB'S *DONE*.

NOW THEN...*ROAST BEEF, POTATOES, GRAVY*, AND I MAKE MY OWN *BREAD*. IF YOU'RE GOING TO BE *FIGHTING* THIS *BEYONDER-MAN* FOR ALL OF US, YOU'LL NEED YOUR STRENGTH.

YOUR CITY IS NOW ON A PLANET CALLED *BATTLE-WORLD*.

WE'RE NOT FIGHTING THE *BEYONDER*, WE'RE FIGHTING A GROUP OF *SUPER VILLAINS*.

WELL, *QUIT FIGHTING ME* AND *GET ON UP THOSE STAIRS!* I *SWEAR* YOU'RE WORSE THAN *HUBERT* WHEN IT COMES TO GETTING YOU INSIDE FOR *DINNER!*

THIS IS MY *HUSBAND, ALBIE,* AND THEN *RACHEL,* AND *JORDAN.*

MOM, IS THAT... *SPIDER-MAN?*

SPIDER-MAN!

ARE YOU *REALLY* SPIDER-MAN?

I *REALLY* AM.

I STILL NEED TO GO FIND *HUBERT.* BACK IN A *FLASH!*

SPIDEY, I'M GETTIN' SOMETHIN' FROM *REED.*

BEN...I'VE BEEN SCANNING THE TERRITORY NEAR *DENVER,* AND THERE'S A *LARGE GROUP OF ALIEN CREATURES* ON THE MOVE NEAR THE OUTSKIRTS OF THE CITY.

THEY DON'T SEEM TO BE A PROBLEM, *YET,* BUT I THOUGHT YOU SHOULD KNOW.

THANKS. KEEP ME UPDATED.

HE MEANS THE *SPINDLIES.*

SPINDLIES?

THAT'S OUR NAME FOR THEM. THEY HAVE *LONG THIN LIMBS.* YOU BOYS WANT *MILK? WATER? JUICE?*

CAN YOU *WALK ON THE WALL?*

YES.

DO IT *NOW!*

JORDAN, LEAVE SPIDER-MAN BE. HE'S GOT *BIGGER WORRIES* THAN *IMPRESSING* NINE-YEAR-OLD BOYS.

THIS IS *LOCKHEED*, ISN'T IT?

YEAH. BELONGS TO *KITTY PRYDE*, THAT GIRL FROM THE *X-MEN.*

WELL, TELL THIS *KITTY GIRL* "*THANK YOU.*" HER DRAGON *SAVED* OUR LIVES.

THESE SPINDLIES SEEM MORE *AGGRESSIVE* THAN REED *WUZ* SAYING. WE MIGHT OUGHTTA *DO SOMETHING* ABOUT THIS.

YEAH, THERE'S THAT, AND THEN--

--YOU GUYS KNOW ALL ABOUT *DOCTOR DOOM* BEING *HERE* IN *DENVER*, RIGHT?

AWWW, NO.

OH. YOU *DIDN'T* KNOW.

YEAH...HE'S HERE. I COULD SHOW YOU. AT MY *GIRLFRIEND'S* PLACE.

THIRTY MINUTES LATER...

YOU HAPPEN TO KNOW THE WOMEN?

MARSHA ROSENBERG AND MARY MACPHERRAN. JULIA, THAT'S MY GIRLFRIEND, DOESN'T REALLY KNOW THEM PAST SAYING HELLO ON THE STREET.

ANYWAY, DOCTOR DOOM HAS BEEN STOPPING BY FOR A FEW DAYS, NOW. SOMETIMES TWO OR THREE TIMES IN ONE DAY.

SO WHAT DO THEY *DO* TOGETHER? DON'T TELL ME *DOCTOR DOOM* IS JUST SITTING AROUND *WATCHING MOVIES OR PLAYIN' CARDS.*

THEY JUST TALK.

YEAH. *NOBODY* PLAYS CARDS WITH DOOM. EVERYONE KNOWS HE *CHEATS.*

SEE, A COUPLE DAYS BACK, MY GIRLFRIEND AND I WERE UP HERE HAVING A PICNIC, AND WE LOOK DOWN ON THAT ROOF, AND THERE'S *DOCTOR DOOM.*

IT'S *HIM* ALL RIGHT. HE'S THE ONLY GUY THAT CAN WALK AROUND IN *THAT MUCH TIN* AND NOT SOUND LIKE SOME-BODY *DROPPED* ALL THEIR POTS AND PANS.

WHAT DO YOU THINK, SPIDEY? SHOULD WE BUST HIM UP ON THIS ONE?

IT ALL SEEMS *CORDIAL* ENOUGH. AND THERE'S ENOUGH TROUBLE IN DENVER RIGHT NOW.

AND THEN THERE'S NOT MUCH CHANCE OF YOU AND I *DOING* MUCH ABOUT IT.

THERE'S THAT.

SO, OKAY, WE LET THIS SLIDE. BUT LET'S KEEP AN EYE ON HIM. TRY TO FIND OUT *WHY* THE DOC'S MAKING HOUSE CALLS.

"I HAVE DISCOVERED A MECHANISM, CRAFTED BY THE BEYONDER, WHICH IS CAPABLE OF BESTOWING INCREDIBLE POWER TO SUCH PERSONS AS I SEE FIT.

"HERE IN DENVER, I HAVE CONTACTED CERTAIN INDIVIDUALS BEST SUITED TO RECEIVE THESE POWERS.

"DURING THE PAST DAYS, I HAVE NARROWED THE FIELD. SOON I WILL TAKE MY PICK."

AND YOU'RE TELLING US THIS BECAUSE...?

BECAUSE IT STRIKES ME THAT YOU YOURSELVES ARE WORTHY CANDIDATES.

SOUNDS TO ME LIKE YOU'RE ABOUT TO OFFER US A CHANCE TO DEAL WITH THE DEVIL.

AND WHY NOT, BEN GRIMM? YOUR STRENGTH HAS VANISHED. WHY NOT REPLACE THEM WITH GREATER POWERS, WHILE STILL RETAINING YOUR HUMANITY?

AND YOU, SPIDER-MAN. THE POWER TO CRUSH YOUR ENEMIES? DOCTOR OCTOPUS, THE LIZARD, THE GREEN GOBLIN, ALL HELPLESS BEFORE YOUR MIGHT?

TOO MUCH FINE PRINT. HAVING YOU AS A BOSS, FOR ONE THING.

BUT IF YOU--

NO.

HSSSSSS

LOCKHEED IS RUNNING OUT OF *FLAMES!*

KEEP HIM *AIRBORNE!* THE THREAT OF HIS FLAMES *STILL* SCARES THEM!

WE CAN'T *WIN* THIS ONE!

PROBABLY *NOT,* BUT WE CAN TAKE A LOT OF *THEM* DOWN WITH US!

HEY, GUYS! *FEEL THE WHEEL!*

SONNY...I SEEN *SATCHEL PAIGE* PITCH BACK IN *'52,* BUT I *AIN'T* NEVER SEEN AN *ARM* LIKE THAT!

THANKS, *GRAMPS!* IF YOU KNOW ANY *BASEBALL SCOUTS,* I'D BE--

LOOK OUT!

BEN!

WHEW!

HOW WE *DOING*, SPIDEY?

WE'RE *HARD PRESSED!* THEY'RE *NOT* THAT *TOUGH*, JUST A *LOT* OF THEM!

DOOM'S CERTAINLY DOING HIS FAIR SHARE.

CAN'T FAULT HIM ON *THAT!*

C'MON...LET'S KEEP THE *PRESSURE* ON THESE *ALIENS!* I THINK THEY'RE *BREAKING!*

HUBERT!

UNNHHH!

DOOM! SAVE THAT KID!

GRUNNNNGHH

THANK YOU.

THEY'RE BREAKING! THE ALIENS ARE RUNNING!

WE'VE BEATEN THEM!

YES, WE *HAVE* WON. AND I HAVE MADE MY *CHOICE.*

MARSHA ROSENBERG. MARY MACPHERRAN. YOU WILL COME WITH ME. YOU HAVE BEEN *CHOSEN.*

BUT WE... WE WEREN'T STRONG ENOUGH TO FIGHT.

AND YET, THE TWO OF YOU *DID* FIGHT. YOUR *CURRENT* FRAILTY IS OF NO MATTER.

I CAN PROVIDE THE *POWER,* NOW THAT *YOU* HAVE SHOWN YOUR DESIRE TO *FIGHT.*

STOP THEM?

NO. WE OWE HIM ONE.

MAYBE, BUT I CAN'T HELP BUT THINK IT MIGHT COME BACK TO BITE US.

YEAH. IT MAY BE THE *RIGHT* THING TO DO, BUT WATCHING *DOOM* WALK OFF LIKE THIS, IT KINDA MAKES ME THINK OF THIS DAY AS A *FAILURE.*

REALLY?

SPIDEY, MAYBE YOU BETTER LOOK *AGAIN.*

BECAUSE GUYS LIKE YOU AND ME, WE TAKE OUR VICTORIES WHERE WE CAN GET 'EM.

AND *I* CAN SEE PLENTY OF PEOPLE WHO THINK TODAY WAS A *COMPLETE* SUCCESS.

...END

RIGHT NOW

SHORTLY... GALACTUS! *GALACTUS!*

HE'S COMPLETELY OBLIVIOUS TO ME-- BUT I *MUST* REACH HIM!

LISTEN TO ME! I THINK I KNOW WHAT YOU'RE PLANNING--AND IT IS *MADNESS!* IT WILL GUARANTEE *YOUR* DEATH AS SURELY AS OURS! YOU *KNOW* THIS--!

BUT, BACK AT MAGNETO'S FORTRESS...

IT IS NO USE! WE'RE LIKE GNATS TO GALACTUS! EVEN AT REST, HIS MENTAL DEFENSES ARE FAR TOO MUCH FOR US!

NO! MAGNETO IS NO INSECT! HE *MUST* ACKNOWLEDGE US!

IF WE MUST, WE'LL *BATTER* OUR WAY THROUGH!

MAGNUS, NO--! YOU'RE CAUSING A *SURGE*--!

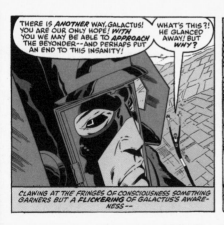

THERE IS *ANOTHER* WAY, GALACTUS! YOU ARE OUR ONLY HOPE! WITH YOU WE MAY BE ABLE TO *APPROACH* THE BEYONDER--AND PERHAPS PUT AN END TO THIS INSANITY!

WHAT'S THIS?! HE GLANCED AWAY! BUT *WHY?*

CLAWING AT THE FRINGES OF CONSCIOUSNESS SOMETHING GARNERS BUT A *FLICKERING* OF GALACTUS'S AWARENESS--

--AND BY SHEER REFLEX, A MASSIVE WAVE OF *PSIONIC FEEDBACK* INUNDATES THE SOURCE OF THE DISTURBANCE--

--WITH *DEVASTATING* EFFECT!

THIS IS SOME WEIRD *REALITY-WARPING* ATTACK FROM *GALACTUS*, ISN'T IT?

YEAH. *SORRY.* YOU DON'T *REALLY* GET TO LIVE WITH ME. THIS IS ALL AN *ILLUSION.*

AM I FIGHTING *KILLER ROBOTS* RIGHT NOW?

NO. ACTUALLY, WE JUST LANDED.

I THOUGHT WE ALREADY *HAD.* I MEAN, I CAN *REMEMBER* ALREADY LANDING. BEING AT THE BASE OF THIS HILL.

VERY POSSIBLE. TIME DOESN'T *HAVE* TO PLAY BY *YOUR* RULES, YOU KNOW. NOT ON *GALACTUS'S* WATCH.

THE *REAL* BATTLE WILL START SOON.

HOW COME YOU *KNOW* ALL THIS? AND *WHY* DO YOU KEEP *SHOWING* UP?

WELL, ROOMIE, AS YOU SAY...I'M THE *ENCHANTRESS.*

AND...?

AND I'M NOT ONLY *IMMORTAL* BUT ALSO *WISE* IN THE *WAYS OF THE MIND.*

MEANING...?

MEANING THAT I'M OF THE FEW PEOPLE WHO CAN KEEP IT *TOGETHER* DURING AN ATTACK FROM GALACTUS, BECAUSE I HAVE MORE *GROUNDING* IN *REALITY.*

RIGHT NOW YOU'RE BATTLING FORCES YOU *CAN'T* COMPREHEND, DOING SO ON *MORE LEVELS* OF *REALITY* THAN YOU KNEW *EXISTED*, AND YOUR MIND IS REACHING OUT FOR *STABILITY*.

SOME OF YOUR FRIENDS ARE PROBABLY GOING INSANE.

NO. *WORSE.* HE *HAS* NO DIMENSIONS.

WHAT WE NORMALLY SEE OF GALACTUS IS THE MEREST TIP. HE'S AN ICEBERG OF COSMIC DIMENSIONS.

NO BOUNDARIES AT ALL.

SPIDER-MAN! IN HERE!

THIS...THIS IS OUR BATTLEWORLD HEADQUARTERS! BUT I... I JUST SAW MYSELF OVER--

NOT SURPRISING. YOU'RE ONLY A WITNESS THIS TIME. THIS IS ONE OF YOUR PERSONAL REALITIES.

MINE? THEN WHY AM I LOOKING AT THOR AND THE HULK?

DON'T ASK ME. IT'S YOUR LIFE.

GREAT. THANKS. YOU COMPLETELY CLEARED THAT UP. SAY...CAN THEY SEE US?

NOT AT ALL. WE'RE IN A SEPARATE REALITY.

HEY! THOR! YOUR CAPE'S BACK! AND YOUR HAT! BUT HOW--? UNLESS YOU'VE GOT A HABERDASHER WHO MAKES FORTRESS CALLS!

T'WAS THE HULK'S DOING-- USING A WONDROUS DEVICE HE DISCOVERED!

IT'S IN THERE, SPIDER-MAN. YOU JUST THINK INTO IT, AND IT PRODUCES ANY SORT OF CLOTH OR CLOTHING YOU WANT.

GREAT! NEW THREADS--WITHOUT STABBING MY THUMB WITH A NEEDLE! THANKS!

HEY, HULK! WHICH OF THESE GIZMOS IS IT?

IT'S THAT ONE. RIGHT THERE.

--AND WE WERE HELPING TO EVACUATE THE VILLAGE.

UHH... YEAH.

HOW'D YOU *KNOW?*

HAD THE *SAME* DREAM. OR... MAYBE THE SAME *REALITY*.

THIS IS REALLY KIND OF *UNNERVING.*

THAT'S THE *THING* ABOUT GALACTUS. THE BATTLE'S *NEVER* REALLY OVER. HE GETS IN YOUR *HEAD.* BRINGS OUT YOUR INNER DEMONS.

YEAH. I SUPPOSE.

NICE *COSTUME,* BY THE WAY.

THANKS.

WELL, THAT'S KIND OF A DOWNER.

...END

SPIDER-MAN, YOU'RE EASILY THE MOST *AMAZING* AND *BELOVED* HERO OF ALL TIME.

CAN YOU EXPLAIN A BIT ABOUT YOUR LIFE, AND YOUR RISE TO ULTIMATE POWER?

EARTH.
NEW PARKER CITY.

ABSOLUTELY, JONAH. FIRST OF ALL, I SHOULD THANK *WOLVERINE.*

OH... HANG ON A MOMENT.

LOOKS LIKE THE *GREEN GOBLIN* MURDERED UNCLE BEN.

NO!

HEE HAAA HEEE HEEE!

NO WORRIES HERE.

I'LL JUST BRING HIM BACK TO LIFE.

I SUPPOSE I SHOULD DO SOMETHING TO PUNISH THE GREEN GOBLIN, TOO.

THAT'S THE RESPONSIBLE THING TO DO, RIGHT?

LET'S TAKE IT *OUTSIDE.* AUNT MAY DOESN'T LIKE IT WHEN I *OBLITERATE* SUPER VILLAINS IN THE HOUSE.

CLICK

CLICK

CLICK

CLICK

UNNNGGH!

WOW. I JUST REALIZED SOMETHING.

I REALLY DON'T LIKE BEING HIT BY ROBOTS!

NONE OF US DO, KID, SO *SHUT UP* AND KEEP MAKING *WRECKAGE!*

REED! WHAT'S OUR *PLAN* HERE? HOW DO WE *REACH GALACTUS?*

DID IT **STOP?** WHAT'S HAPPENING?

SOMETHING'S GONE **WRONG.** SOMETHING **INTERRUPTED** THE PROCESS. I BELIEVE SOMEONE IS **DIVERTING** GALACTUS'S POWER. MAYBE EVEN... **STEALING** IT?

IT WAS QUITE PERCEPTIVE OF REED RICHARDS, FOR THAT IS **PRECISELY** WHAT WAS HAPPENING.

I WAS STEALING THE POWER OF GALACTUS IN ORDER THAT I MIGHT CHALLENGE THE **GREATER POWER** OF THE BEYONDER.

I KNOW I SHOULDN'T WONDER AT REED'S DEDUCTIONS. AT THIS MOMENT, WITH MY COSMIC AWARENESS, I DO RECOGNIZE THAT, OF THE TWO OF US, HE HAS **ALWAYS** BEEN THE **SMARTER** MAN.

HIS INTELLIGENCE IS RATHER **HUMBLING.**

OF COURSE, TO BE **HUMBLED** IS TO ADMIT **DEFEAT.** BUT...NO MATTER.

PERHAPS IT WAS MY **AWE** OVER RICHARDS'S **INTELLECT** THAT PUT THE FIRST SEEDS OF SELF-DOUBT INTO MY OWN MIND...CAUSING ME TO CAST A **SCENT** FROM WOLVERINE'S PAST INTO THE AIR...**LURING** HIM INTO MY BATTLE WITH THE BEYONDER.

JEAN?

BUT MORE LIKELY HE WAS ALERTED BY MY OWN HIDDEN FEARS OF FAILURE.

PETER?

GWEN?

THOSE FEARS, MY MEREST UNCONSCIOUS WHIM...CAUSED FLICKERS OF MY VAST POWERS TO REACH OUT AND **BETRAY** ME DURING A MOMENT OF **WEAKNESS,** CREATING **PHANTOMS** THAT WOULD ALSO ALERT **SPIDER-MAN** TO MY PLANS.

JEAN!

WAIT! WAIT!

OH!

GWEN! I-- WHERE DID YOU...?

WOLVERINE! DID YOU SEE A BLONDE GIRL? IN BOOTS? A GREEN COAT AND--

NO. DID YOU SEE A WOMAN WITH LONG RED HAIR? HER SCENT IS...GONE. THERE'S NO TRACE! THAT'S NOT EVEN POSSI--

WHOA!

HOLD ON, SPIDEY!

THAT GIRL! IS SHE THE ONE YOU WERE TALKING ABOUT?

NO. THE SCENT IS WRONG. SOMEBODY'S PLAYING A GAME WITH US.

ANY GUESSES AS TO WHO?

A POSSIBILITY COMES TO MIND, YEAH.

DURING OUR BATTLE OF WILLS, I HELD LESS DOUBT THAN THE BEYONDER.

AS EVER, LOST IN THE CHAOS OF COMBAT, I WAS *MYSELF*.

EVEN AS SPIDER-MAN AND WOLVERINE FOUGHT THEIR OWN BATTLES--

I WAS DRIVING THE *BEYONDER* TO HIS *KNEES*, TAKING HIS *POWER*.

PERHAPS THE POWER GOES TO THE ONE IT FEELS IS THE MOST *DESERVING*, AND CERTAINLY IN THOSE MOMENTS, *DOOM'S* WILL WAS *SUPREME*.

THE POWER *LEFT* THE BEYONDER. AND WAS *DESTINED* FOR *MYSELF*.

BUT FIRST, A *DETOUR*.

AT LEAST, I WAS ABLE TO TAKE IT FOR A MOMENT.

THIS IS A POWER *BEYOND* ANYONE'S CONTROL. A POWER THAT *CANNOT* REMAIN *MINE.*

JUST AS THEY DID FOR *WOLVERINE* AND *SPIDER-MAN,* MY OWN *SELF DOUBT* AND MY *FEARS* WILL ATTAIN REALITY...

GIVEN LIFE BY THE *CHAOS* OF MY MIND...

FUELED BY THE BEYONDER'S POWERS, AND THESE DOUBTS *WILL* DEFEAT ME.

PERHAPS MY FEARS WILL MANIFEST AS *RICHARDS.* OR IT MAY BE *CAPTAIN AMERICA* WHO *BESTS* ME.

EVEN *NOW,* WITH ALL THESE *POWERS,* I FIND I CANNOT *TRULY* BELIEVE MYSELF CAPABLE OF DEFEATING SUCH MEN. THEY *ALWAYS* FIND A WAY.

IN THE MEANTIME, BEFORE I AM CONQUERED, BEFORE THE INEVITABLE MOMENT WHEN THE BEYONDER REGAINS HIS POWERS, I HAVE ALTERED REALITY ONCE MORE.

THE MINDS OF THESE TWO MEN CANNOT BEAR SUCH BURDENS AS I HAVE GIVEN THEM. THUS, AS A *GIFT* FOR THEIR *SERVICE,* I WILL ERASE ALL THAT HAS GONE BEFORE.

IT SHALL BE AS THOUGH THEY NEVER ACCOMPANIED ME ON THIS PATH TO GODHOOD--

--NOR PROVIDED AN EXAMPLE FOR MY EVENTUAL DOWNFALL.

--SHUT UP AND KEEP MAKING WRECKAGE!

THAT'S THE LAST OF THEM! C'MON! LET'S JOIN THE OTHERS!

IF GALACTUS MANAGES TO STEAL THIS PLANET'S ENERGY WE--

YOU OKAY?

MY CLAWS KEEP POPPING OUT. CAN'T QUITE CONTROL THEM.

SNIKT

SNIKT

YOU MUST HAVE TAKEN SOME INTERNAL DAMAGE DURING THE FIGHT. MAYBE YOU SHOULD--

SPIDEY... DON'T WORRY ABOUT IT. TRUST ME.

WHATEVER HAPPENED...I HEAL FAST.

...END

CHARACTER SKETCHES BY PATRICK SCHERBERGER

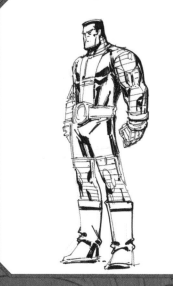

COLOSSUS

HUBERT

CAPTAIN MARVEL

CAPTAIN MARVEL

ROGUE

SPINDLIES

STORM

WASP